JOHN THOMPSON'S MODERN COURSE FOR THE PIANO

TEACHING LITTLE FINGERS TO PLAY

NOTE TO PARENTS

This is your child's FIRST PIANO BOOK.

As a parent you have a right to expect progress. If you will assist the teacher by arousing your child's interest and enthusiasm in each successive lesson, the result will speak for itself.

Words have been added to most of the musical examples to help interpret the spirit of the little melodies. So READ THEM to the youngster and EXPLAIN their meaning. These melodies were written with careful thought and were kept as simple as possible in order to keep them within the grasp of a child's hand, which is quite naturally, small. Help the student play in strict time. Even if you do not play piano yourself, it will be fun.

DUET PLAYING FOR PARENT AND PUPIL

Parents who play the piano even a little are advised to examine a supplementary book to "TEACHING LITTLE FINGERS TO PLAY," called "TEACHING LITTLE FINGERS TO PLAY ENSEMBLE." This is a separate book containing duet-accompaniments that have been arranged to supply the harmonies for use with each little melody found in "TEACHING LITTLE FINGERS TO PLAY." By using the supplementary book, parents or teacher may play DUETS with the child from the very beginning. The attractiveness of playing with someone else is very strong to any young beginner who finds the study of piano a bit lonesome at the start. It is also one of the most delightful means of enjoying music in the home and, incidentally, develops strict observance of rhythm and quick thinking.

Psychologists claim that the hazard of loneliness in piano study is a very real one, and "TEACHING LITTLE FINGERS TO PLAY ENSEMBLE" banishes this obstacle to the happy progress of the child.

Ask your teacher or music dealer to show you the book called "TEACHING LITTLE FINGERS TO PLAY ENSEMBLE".

THE WILLIS MUSIC COMPANY   **FLORENCE, KENTUCKY 41042**

Cover, Design & Illustrations By Nicholas E. Gressle ©1994

TO THE TEACHER
HOW TO PRESENT THE FIRST THREE LESSONS IN *TEACHING LITTLE FINGERS TO PLAY*

When children can place their tiny fingers on the piano keyboard and PLAY A TUNE during the first few moments of their first lesson they discover that to learn music is as easy as any play-time activity. Hence, the advisability of TEACHING BY ROTE.

This book incorporates rote teaching, the ADVANTAGE of this being that the pupil cheerfully makes music while simultaneously mastering the necessary rudiments required to PLAY BY NOTE.

The following procedure, if carefully observed, will teach any pupil to MAKE MUSIC FIVE MINUTES after the first lesson, and by the fourth lesson the pupil will be able to PLAY BY NOTE.

FIRST LESSON

The musical examples in the first three lessons are to be taught ENTIRELY BY ROTE (i.e., imitation). The purpose is to teach the NAMES OF THE KEYS ONLY. The notes will be learned later.

1. Teach *Stepping* and *Skipping*, first as a song. The teacher plays and sings a few times until the pupil memorises both TUNE and WORDS. (The pupil is already making music.)
When the pupil can SING it correctly, teach him to PLAY it on the piano by *finger patterns*.

2. Teach the *number names* of the fingers.

Left Hand   Right Hand

3. Teacher PLAYS and SINGS the *first pattern* slowly using the number names of the fingers thus:

4. When the pupil can *imitate* the first pattern, PLAY and SING the second pattern the same way and have the pupil imitate.

FIRST PATTERN

SING: ONE TWO THREE

SECOND PATTERN

SING: THREE TWO ONE

5. Now PLAY and SING the *third pattern* and have the pupil imitate in exactly the same way.

THIRD PATTERN

SING: TWO THREE ONE

6. When the pupil can play all three patterns using the number names of the fingers, then teach him or her to play and sing the *letter names of the keys*:

SING: C D E   E D C   D E   C
PLAY:

7. After the pupil has played the three patterns, first with the RIGHT HAND and then with the LEFT HAND ALONE, he or she should be instructed to play them in different octaves on the keyboard; see example below.

RIGHT HAND

SING: C D E   E D C   D E   C

LEFT HAND

SING: C D E   E D C   D E   C

TO THE TEACHER (Continued)

The pupil has sung and played a tune in much less time than it has taken to describe. He or she has played with the LEFT and RIGHT hands and developed the first three fingers of each hand equally.

THE PUPIL HAS LEARNED TO RECOGNISE AND PLAY THREE KEYS ON THE KEYBOARD

THE LESSON IN NOTATION

The first lesson is very simple. The pupil is taught to recognise the TREBLE and BASS CLEF signs, BAR LINES and BARS as illustrated on page 5. Teachers usually have individual methods for teaching the rudiments; hence, all examples are subject to the effect of a suggestion - the success of your own individuality.

SECOND LESSON

Proceed exactly as in Lesson One. First as a SONG, then by FINGER PATTERNS (*pupil singing number names of fingers*). Finally as shown in example (*pupil now singing letter names of keys*).

After the pupil can play the example with each hand separately in various octaves COMBINE GROUPS 2 and 1 as follows:

SING:

The pupil has learned FIVE keys on the keyboard - A B C D E - and can PLAY and SING a tune of 8 bars, using both hands.

THE LESSON IN NOTATION

In this second lesson, the pupil is taught to recognise and know the value of CROTCHETS, MINIMS and SEMI-BREVES.

(The crotchet is used as a unit instead of the semi-breve to avoid fractions. "ONE NOTE, ONE COUNT," is easily understood, whereas when the semi-breve is taught first, the child is asked to *divide a note in his mind* into four fractional parts.)

THIRD LESSON

Teach the remaining letter - names E F G by presenting Stepping and Skipping on the new keys as in other lessons. When the example can be played with either hand in various octaves COMBINE GROUPS 3 and 1 as follows:

The pupil now learns TIME SIGNATURES in the LESSON IN NOTATION (pg. 7). He has learned all 7 white keys — A B C D E F G, has been making music for three lessons and has absorbed enough knowledge of NOTATION to enable him or her to read without dictation from now on. Thus ROTE TEACHING has been used as a MEANS TOWARD AN END.

(NOTE: — After the third lesson, material should be assigned according to the capacity of each individual pupil)

4

Contents
"Something New Every Lesson"

Teachers who, for the sake of thoroughness, desire to have the pupil practice writing BAR LINES, CLEFS, TIME SIGNATURES, etc., etc., will find "JOHN THOMPSON'S NOTE SPELLER" very useful. — J.T.

FIRST LESSON AT THE KEYBOARD

LEARNING THE KEYS C D E

The **BLACK** keys of the piano keyboard are divided into patterns of **TWO** and **THREE**. To the left of the TWO **BLACK** key pattern, in the centre of your piano under the maker's name, is **MIDDLE C**.

Locate, and play MIDDLE C with the FIRST finger (*THUMB*) of your RIGHT hand.

MIDDLE C D E

D is between

To the RIGHT of the TWO BLACK key pattern is E

Stepping and Skipping

Step-ping up,   Step-ping down, Then   a   skip.

(1) Learn first as a SONG. (2) PLAY and SING the words. (3) Play and sing the letter-names of the KEYS. (4) Play each hand separately in VARIOUS OCTAVES

LEFT HAND

RIGHT HAND

FIRST LESSON IN NOTATION
Learning the Grand Staff, Clef Signs and Bars

TREBLE CLEF
SIGN

BAR
LINE

BAR
LINE

BAR
LINE

DOUBLE
BAR LINE

BASS CLEF

← BAR →   ← BAR →   ← BAR →   ← BAR →

Always placed at the
end of a piece
of music.

SECOND LESSON AT THE KEYBOARD

NEW KEYS A, B, and playing A B C

B's neighbour is A

To the RIGHT of the three BLACK Key pattern is B

Always **B**e **C**urious
to find other A, B, C's on the keyboard

Stepping and Skipping from A

Step - ping up,   Step-ping down, Then   a   skip.

Combining Group 2 and Group 1

GROUP 1

GROUP 2

SECOND LESSON IN NOTATION:
Notes, like Coins, have different values

A CROTCHET IS HELD FOR **1 COUNT**

A MINIM IS HELD FOR **2 COUNTS**

A SEMI-BREVE IS HELD FOR **4 COUNTS**

New Keys F, G and playing E F G

To the LEFT of the three BLACK Key pattern is F

F's neighbour is G

Always
Be
Curious
to find other E, F, G's
on the keyboard

Stepping and Skipping from E

Step-ping up, Step-ping down, Then a skip.

Combining Group 3 and 1

GROUP 3 - Play with right hand

GROUP 1 - Play with left hand

THIRD LESSON IN NOTATION

The TIME SIGNATURE next to the CLEF sign at the beginning of a piece tells us how it should be counted.

Upper figure means that there are two counts to a bar.

Lower figure means that each crotchet gets one count.

Count: 1 2 1 2

THREE Counts to a bar.

Crotchet gets one count.

Count: 1 2 3 1 2 3

FOUR counts to a bar.

Crotchet gets one count.

Count: 1 2 3 4 1 2 3 4 1234

Birthday Party

Right hand GROUP for this piece.
Locate C D E in other parts
of keyboard

Strong beat   Weak beat

Here   we   go,   Up   a   row

To   a   birth - day   par -   ty.

Left hand GROUP for this piece. Locate and play A B C in other parts of the keyboard.

Sandman's Near

Dol - ly dear, Sand-man's near,

You will soon be sleep - ing.

Baseball Days

Come on kids, join the fun,

Base - ball days have be - gun.

When the stem of Middle C goes
Up play it with the right hand.
When the stem of Middle C goes
Down play it with the left hand.

L.H. Group   **R.H. Group**

Upper figure means that there are 3 counts in each bar.

Lower figure means that each crotchet gets one count.

THE DOTTED MINIM
(THREE-BEAT NOTE)

HOLD 3 BEATS (1,2,3).
A DOT after a note increases its value half the value of the note before it.

The Postman

Post-man I'll   be   one day   when I grow   tall;   letsgo

Let-ters I'll   bring you in   win-ter and   fall.

In 3-4 Time be sure to accent the first beat of each bar.

Rain on the Roof

**4 Counts to each bar.
Crotchet gets one count.**

**4/4 Time has one strong beat
and three weak beats.**

Pit-ter, pat-ter, go the rain-drops on the tin roof fall-ing,

I can hear their ti-ny voic-es call-ing, call-ing, call-ing.

**Mark the Left hand and Right
hand GROUPS yourself.**

The Dotted Minim ♩ In Four-Four Time.

Song of the Volga Boatmen

Yo, yo, heave ho! Oh, yo, yo, heave ho! So

pull to - geth - er; for - ward still we go.

M usic is written in HAPPY KEYS (*Major*) and SAD keys (*Minor*).

This famous Russian Folk-Song is an example in a SAD key.

Years ago, before there were steamboats, the peasants who lived along the banks of the Volga used to pull boats and barges, heavily loaded with merchandise, up the river from one village to the next.

The plodding along the banks of those condemned to this labour was terrible. While struggling along they used to lighten their burden by singing the sad strains of this rhythmical melody.

14

Groups of notes, like words in books,
tell stories when arranged in sentences
and punctuated.
A curved line over groups of notes indicates
MUSICAL SENTENCES called PHRASES.

A Message

English Folk-Tune

Tap, tap, tap, tap, | someone's knock-ing | at my door to | bring a let-ter,

Tap, tap, tap, tap, | I wish they'd ring; | Our bell sounds much | bet-ter.

Chimes

Good King Wenceslas

THIS very ancient tune was a great favourite among the carol singers who used to beg for alms many centuries ago. It is based on the legend of King Wenceslas, the Holy, who was king of Bohemia in the Tenth Century. On the feast of St. Stephen (Dec. 26) this good king went out among the poor and gave liberally.

English Christmas Carol

Good King Wen - ces - las look'd out On the feast of Ste - phen,

Where the snow lay round a bout, Deep and crisp - and e - ven.

In music notation there are also SIGNS of SILENCE, called RESTS, which tell us when and how many beats our fingers should be silent, viz.:

	CROTCHET REST	MINIM REST	SEMI-BREVE REST
Pictures of RESTS	𝄽	▬	▬
Relative NOTE value	♩	♪	o
BEATS (Count)	1	1, 2	1, 2, 3, 4

Lazy Mary

READ and name the four notes above and three notes below MIDDLE C. Count as you play.

Betty and Bill

Flying to the Moon

American Folk Tune
(Adapted)

Shall we go a - fly - ing, fly - ing, fly - ing?

Shall we go a - fly - ing to the moon?

The time value of a quaver is HALF as long as that of a crotchet. Play TWO quavers to ONE count.

PAPA HAYDN", as Mozart lovingly called this great musician, inherited his sense of humor and genius from his father, Mathias Haydn, who was a hard-working and jolly man. He lived in Rohrau, a small Austrian village where, in a combination shop and home, he made and repaired wheels. He had a fine tenor voice and was the sexton and organist in the village church. His wife sang in the choir.

Young Joseph had eleven brothers and sisters. At the age of 5 he was taken to a nearby village where he was taught music. He was always full of mischief and one day as a result of a prank, he was turned out into the stormy night—homeless.

The following morning, he went to a friend, a wigmaker and barber, who let him use his garret. Here, on a dilapidated harpsichord, with snow blowing through the cracks of the roof, Joseph worked and studied.

On moonlight nights he and his friends used to stroll about the streets of Vienna serenading famous musicians. After years of hard work he wrote some of the most magnificent compositions known.

Air
(from Surprise Symphony)

PREPARATION

LOCATE, NAME and PLAY the THREE G's.

LOCATE, NAME and PLAY the TWO C's.

Play and name the first L.H. group, then the second L.H. group and the R.H. group.

By the Pond

Always
Be
Curious
to find other F♯
BLACK keys on the piano.

This sign ♯ is called a SHARP. In this piece you will see it in the first and fifth bars in front of F.
It means to play the BLACK key to the right of F instead of the white key F.

L.H. Group   R.H. Group - Note BLACK KEY

Paper Ships

When I launch my   pa - per ships in   moth - er's shin - y   pail,   Ah,

How I wish I   were a cap - tain   real - ly un - der   sail.

3 counts

Sledding

When the SHARP sign # is placed between the Clef sign and the time signature it becomes the KEY SIGNATURE. In this piece ALL F's must be sharpened—*played on **BLACK** key F*.

Snow - flakes fall - ing fluff - y and white;

O, what fun! We're sled - ding to - night.

Note: — This piece contains the SCALE OF G MAJOR. Those who desire to introduce scales at this stage of instruction may have their pupils make good use of "PETER'S BLANK MUSIC BOOK" (wide ruling).

The Butterfly

But - ter - fly   bright in   the   sun - light,

play - ing,   sway - ing,   Fly - ing from   flow - er   to   flow - er,

blithe   and   gay.

THE TIE

The TIE is a curved line joining one note to another of the SAME PITCH and means that the second note is to be held *for its full value without being struck.*

PREPARATION
Locate, name and play the L.H. Group and then the R.H. Group

L.H. Group

R.H. Group

Questions

Dwarf

"Gi - ant, why are you so tall?"

Giant

"Well, sir, why are you so small?"

Blue-Bells of Scotland

C♯ (Sharp)
Look and listen for Black Middle C

O where, and O where is your High-land lad-die gone? O where, and O

where is your High-land lad- die gone? He's gone to fight the foe for King

George up-on the throne; And it's Oh! in my heart, I wish him safe at home!

Toy Soldiers

Big Ships

Always
Be
Careful

to look and listen for the
FLAT, SHARP, and NATURAL

This ♭ is the **BLACK** key sign called FLAT. It means that you must play the first **BLACK** key to the LEFT of the white key **A** in this piece.

This ♮ sign is a NATURAL which means that when you see it in front of a note that has been played on a **BLACK** key you must play it on its NATURAL, the white key.

Steam-boat Round the Bend

Comin' Round the Mountain

SECONDO

(For Teacher or Slightly Advanced Pupil)

Comin' Round the Mountain

PRIMO

As lively as possible

Southern Mountain Song

B♭ in the key signature means that you must play all B's on the BLACK key to the LEFT of the white key B.

Repeat ad lib.

The Long Trail

Hik- ing the   trails of the   Rock - ies,   lots   of   fun.

Climb-ing up   hill ver - y   slow - ly,   come   down on the   run.

"A" SHARP is the first BLACK KEY to the Right of A

Skipping SPACE notes F and A

The Bee

This piece begins on a weak beat—the last count in a bar. You must therefore ACCENT the first beat after the bar line. The missing counts of the first bar will be found in the last bar of the piece.

My Bonnie

8······means: Play EIGHT keys higher

Vacation Time

I'm waltz - ing a - round in a mer - ry mood, I'm hav - ing a great deal of

fun,_____ There's nev - er a cloud in the sky to - day, Va -

ca - tion has be - gun._____

Home on the Range

SECONDO
Teacher or slightly advanced pupil

Slowly with much expression

Cowboy Ballad

Home on the Range

PRIMO

Slowly with much expression

Cowboy Ballad

D.S. al Fine—go back to the 𝄋 sign and play until the **Fine.**

The Juggler

Jug - gler, Jug - gler, what's your name?

L.H. over

L.H. over

All the cir - cus post - ers

ad - ver - tise your fame!

If I tried to toss a cup,

L.H. over

L.H. over

I would on - ly have to pick the piec - es up.

R.H. over

Play both keys together

R.H. Group.

E♭ is the 1st BLACK key to the LEFT of E.

From a Wigwam

CERTIFICATE of MERIT

This certifies that

....

has successfully completed

TEACHING LITTLE FINGERS TO PLAY

and is eligible for promotion to
"JOHN THOMPSON'S FIRST GRADE BOOK"

....

Teacher

....

Date